# Latina Looks Like Me

## "Latina como yo"

By Rukia K

Illustrated by: Graphii

**Latina Looks Like Me**
Latina como yo

Copyright © 2021 by Rukia K
Illustrated by: Graphii
ISBN: 978-0-578-82589-2

Latina Looks Like Me™ is a culturally relevant book written to empower Latinas of all ages. It is intended to celebrate their exquisite uniqueness, (or unique beauty) and to promote diversity, equity, and inclusivity for all. The message in this book in no way is intended to be exclusive of any ethnicity represented in the Latino community.

First and foremost, I want to give honor and thanks to God for using me as a vessel to see and carry this vision into fruition. Without Him, I am nothing!

This book is dedicated to my inner child, whose voice is very much a part of who I am today. 10-year-old Rukia has inspired me to write this book, and I am so happy that I listened to you and trusted you!

A mi Madre, who is from Panamá —y a mi FAMILIA ENTERA!—thank you for always supporting me and encouraging me. You all have inspired me in so many ways... THIS IS FOR YOU!

To my father and my entire family from Tanzania: you all are a part of what has shaped me to become the woman I am today. I am equally proud to be African, as much as I am to be Latina.

To my son, Mark: I hope this project inspires you to reach for your dreams, no matter how big they may seem. Always stay true to who you are and trust yourself. You inspire me in so many ways. I am so proud to be your mommy!

To my Tribe: thank you for being honest and sharing your thoughts. Thank you for being my unofficial editors and biggest critics...haha... Thank you for keeping me grounded, and most importantly, thank you for loving me for me!

To anyone else who has encouraged me and believed in this idea from its inception: I thank you all from the bottom of my heart!

# My Skin Tone
## El color de mi piel

• • • • ♥ • • • •

My skin can be the color of ground coriander,
cinnamon, nutmeg, or even dark cocoa. It is as
warm as the sand, or as deep as the Earth's soil.

It embraces and traces far back as history will tell.
Once you know me, you will know this well.

But if you do not, just look, and you will see.
Latina is diverse, just like me!

# My Hair
## Mi cabello

My hair is my crown.
It is beautiful: whether it is black,
blond, red, or brown.

I adore it, no matter its shape.
It can be curly, wavy, or straight.

My crown: I am proud to wear all the time.
I am so happy that my hair is mine.

When you look at me, you will see,
Latinas have gorgeous hair, just like me!

# My Shape
## La forma de mi cuerpo

Thin or thick, with a few extra pounds,
Latinas are beautiful however they are.

With hearts that glitter and smiles that shine,
I love the way I am; this is my design.

We love our bodies: we stand bold with beauty.
We are fearfully & wonderfully made; and
just like us, you are all unique.

Latinas come in multiple shapes and
sizes, just like me!

# My Eyes
## Mis ojos

• • • • • ♥ • • • • •

When you see Latina, what do you see?
Did you know that Latina can look like me?

Our eyes are the windows;
we have to see the world.
Blue like the ocean, green like the trees,
or frosty like ice, we use them to see.

Take a look and see:
Latinas have beautiful eyes, just like me!

# My Lips
## Mis labios

Our lips can express the joy from deep within,
with laughter, or a slight grin.

Thick or thin, narrow or wide,
our beautiful lips, we cannot hide.

When we laugh, our faces are filled with glee.
We love to smile, proud as can be.

Latinas smile, just like me!

# My Nose
## Mi nariz

• • • • • ♥ • • • • •

There are flat, wide, pointy, slender,
small, and button noses.

Different shapes, different sizes,
to help us sniff the beautiful roses.

Small or wide, a Latina's confidence,
we will not hide.

Along with our other facial features
that make up our beauty, Latinas love
their unique noses, just like me!

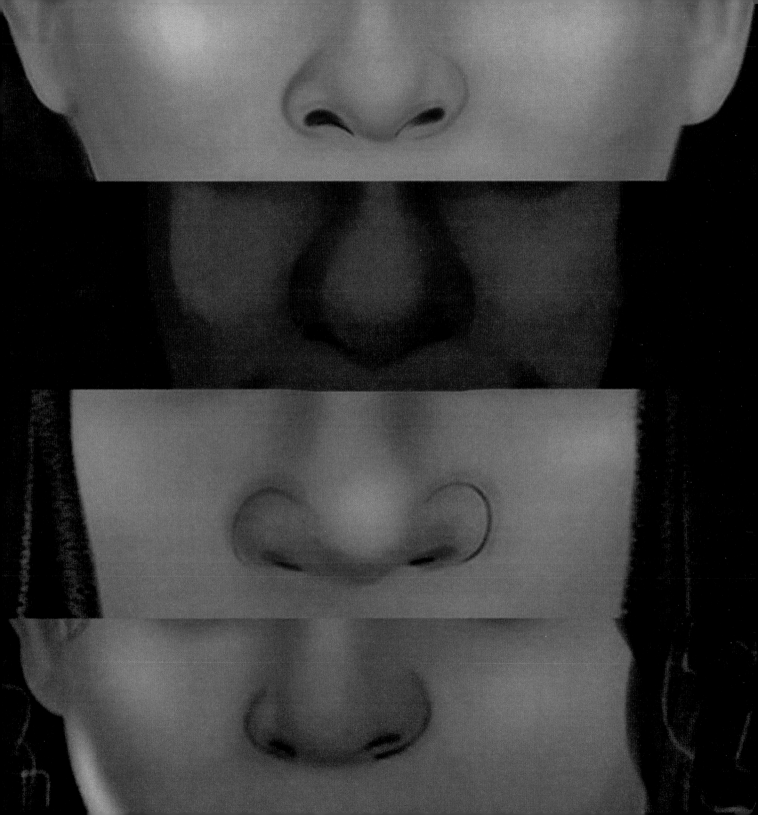

# My Face
## Mi cara

Take a look, it's all in this space:
unique and lovely are a Latina's face.

Round or long, whatever your shape,
I want you to know that you are filled with grace.

Freckles or not, or even a few spots,
beautiful faces are what we've got.

Whether dark or light, full or petite,
Latinas love their faces, just like me!

# My Language
## Mi idioma

Do you know Latinas can
speak one of several languages?
Latinas speak French, Italian,
Portuguese, Spanish, or even English.

With grace, we embrace different
languages in this beautiful world.
Whatever language we speak,
you know we adore.

Latinas' voices shine bright like the stars above.
Whenever you see me, and you hear me speak,
know that Latina sounds just like me!

Every Latina is unique!
It is time for the world to see that
Latinas can look like you or me!

Embrace every bit of you.
Shine bright! Shine true!

So, here is to all Latinas, near and far:
you are enough to be who you are!

Made in the USA
Las Vegas, NV
03 December 2021

35931881R00017